Dear Parents,

Welcome to the Scholastic Reader series. We have taken over 80 years of experience with teachers, parents, and children and put it into a program that is designed to match your child's interests and skills.

Level 1—Short sentences and stories made up of words kids can sound out using their phonics skills and words that are important to remember.

Level 2—Longer sentences and stories with words kids need to know and new "big" words that they will want to know.

Level 3—From sentences to paragraphs to longer stories, these books have large "chunks" of text and are made up of a rich vocabulary.

Level 4—First chapter books with more words and fewer pictures.

It is important that children learn to read well enough to succeed in school and beyond. Here are ideas for reading this book with your child:

- Look at the book together. Encourage your child to read the title and make a prediction about the story.
- Read the book together. Encourage your child to sound out words when appropriate. When your child struggles, you can help by providing the word.
- Encourage your child to retell the story. This is a great way to check for comprehension.

Scholastic Readers are designed to support your child's efforts to learn how to read at every age and every stage. Enjoy helping your child learn to read and love to read.

—Francie Alexander
Chief Education Officer
Scholastic Education

Ms. Frizzle

Liz

Written by Anne Capeci
Illustrated by Carolyn Bracken

Based on *The Magic School Bus* books
written by Joanna Cole and illustrated by Bruce Degen

The author would like to thank Mary Delahanty of Antioch University
for her expert advice in preparing this manuscript.

ISBN-13: 978-0-439-89936-9
ISBN-10: 0-439-89936-2

12 11 10 9 8   10 11 12 13 14/0

Designed by Rick DeMonico

First printing, March 2007   Printed in the U.S.A.   40

The Magic School Bus
Gets Recycled

Arnold   Ralphie   Keesha   Phoebe   Carlos   Tim   Wanda   Dorothy Ann

Cartwheel
·B·O·O·K·S·®

SCHOLASTIC INC.
New York   Toronto   London   Auckland   Sydney
Mexico City   New Delhi   Hong Kong   Buenos Aires

We have lots of fun in Ms. Frizzle's class.
Ms. Frizzle wears funny clothes and funny shoes.
She takes us on trips in the Magic School Bus.
We have been collecting things to recycle.
Today is pickup day.

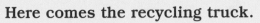

Our trash goes onto the truck.
"These things won't get thrown away,"
Ms. Frizzle tells us.
"They will be used again."

"Don't worry, Phoebe," Ms. Frizzle says.
"We'll get your necklace back.
Get on the bus, kids!"

The Magic School Bus takes off . . . into the air!
It gets small.
A piece of paper blows toward us.
We ride on top of it.

The truck drives into the recycling plant.
When it stops, we catch up.
Paper, bottles, cans, and cartons are piled high.

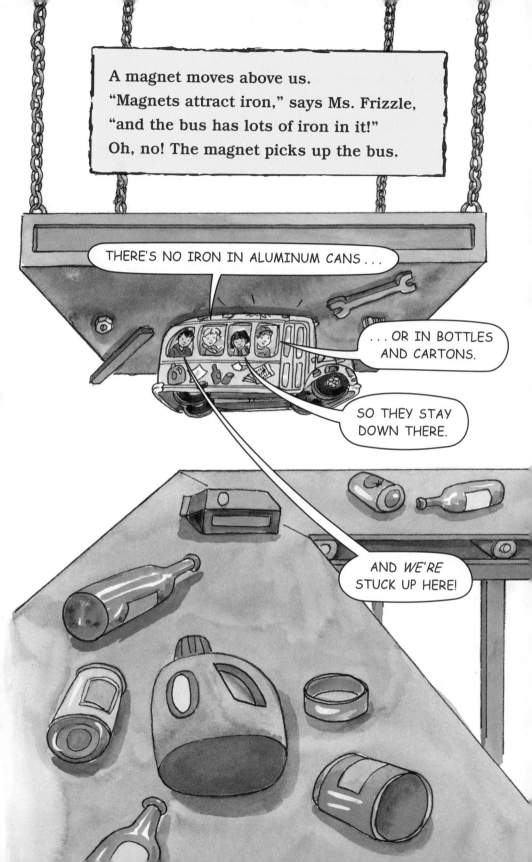

The newspapers go on a truck.
We go, too.
Good-bye, recycling center!

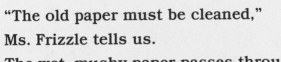

"The old paper must be cleaned,"
Ms. Frizzle tells us.
The wet, mushy paper passes through a screen.
String, glue, and paper clips are too big.
The screen catches them.

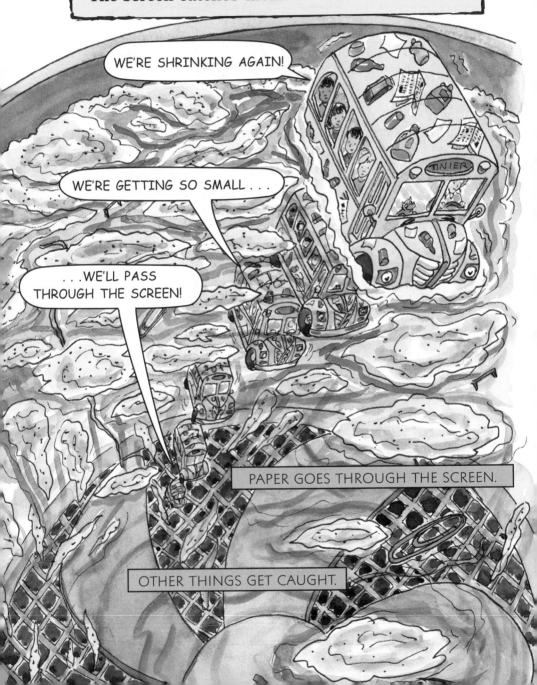

WE'RE SHRINKING AGAIN!

WE'RE GETTING SO SMALL . . .

. . .WE'LL PASS THROUGH THE SCREEN!

PAPER GOES THROUGH THE SCREEN.

OTHER THINGS GET CAUGHT.

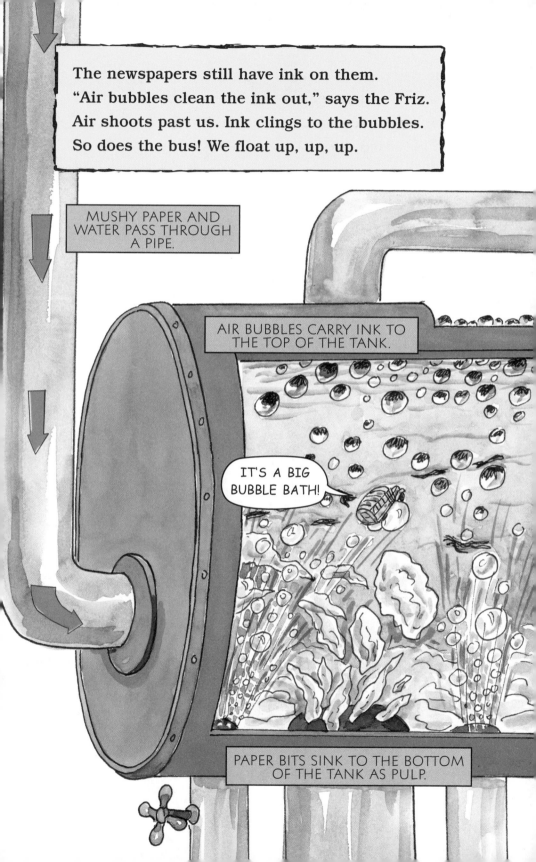

The paper is all clean.

The wet, mushy paper is molded into egg cartons.

The egg cartons are put into a dryer.

We get dried, too!

DRYING
MACHINE

The bus flies out of the dryer.
It gets big again.

HOW EGG-CITING!

THE OLD NEWSPAPERS ARE
SOMETHING NEW NOW.

FINISHED EGG CARTONS

The bus drives out of the paper factory.
The necklace was not in the newspapers.
Then Phoebe looks down.

At school, we make posters about recycling.
Where will we go next?
We can't wait to find out!

HERE ARE SOME FUN WAYS YOU CAN RECYCLE AND REUSE MATERIALS AT HOME!

Use baby food jars to hold paint.

Use CD cases to make picture frames.

1. Tape a photo to a piece of construction paper.
2. Put the paper and photo inside your CD case.
3. Glue a piece of string or ribbon to the back of the CD case so you can hang it up!

Use egg cartons as seed starters.